THE WORLD I SEE

A Story for Children Who Have Felt The Impact of Domestic Violence

Written by Debra Whiting Alexander, Ph.D.
Designed by Beth Weiner Lipson

©Copyright 1992
ISBN 1-56688-054-8

THE BUREAU™ FOR AT-RISK YOUTH

PROMOTING GROWTH THROUGH KNOWLEDGE

135 Dupont Street, Plainview, N.Y. 11803-0760
1-800-99-YOUTH

This Book Belongs To:

_____

The world I see changes everyday.

I never know if it will look happy or mad. The world I see scares me.

A Draw and Color Page

One day on TV I saw somebody mean hurt somebody nice.
It made me feel afraid. My friend said, "Don't be scared!
That's only pretend!"

It's pretend on TV but at my house it's real.

I've seen it happen lots of times. Hitting and yelling, and crying. Once, I saw someone's blood.

I lie awake at night and try not to listen. Sometimes, I'm so afraid I can hardly breathe. And I wonder what will happen to me.

My counselor said that's why I "jump" a lot and feel my heart beat fast. She said our hearts and feelings can get hurt by what we see or hear.

Sometimes, my body gets hurt too.

A Draw and Color Page

My counselor said violence is real. That means some people hurt each other on purpose. She said that sometimes mommies and daddies need help learning how to be angry in a safe way. And it's not okay for us to stay together when we can't be safe.

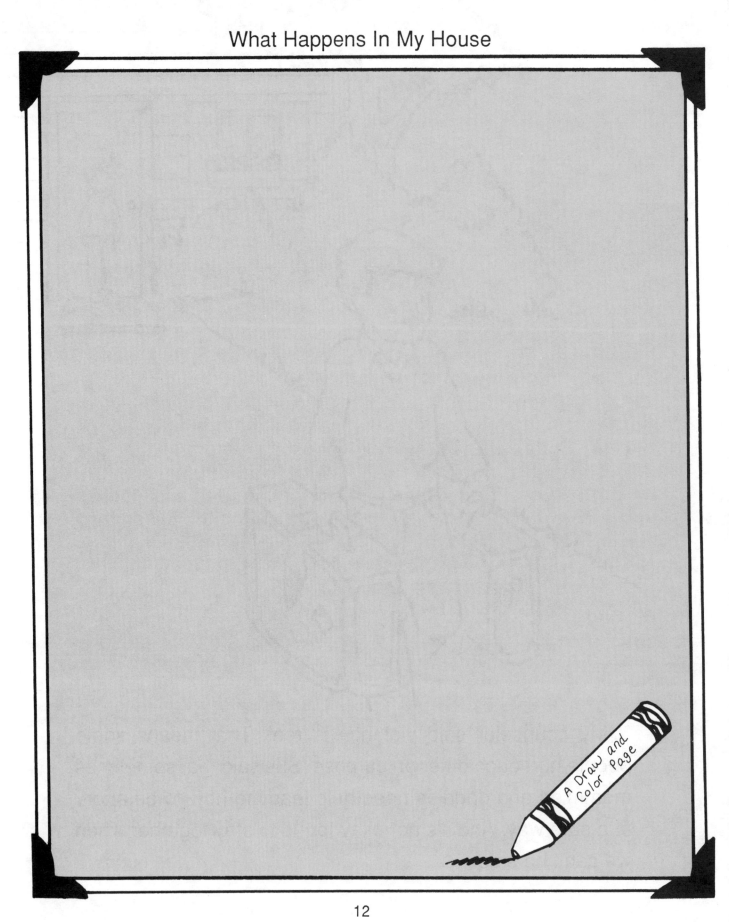

A Draw and Color Page

I know all about fighting! I told my counselor I could fight anyone, even a giant muscle man! I drew pictures to show her how I would do it.

13

A Draw and Color Page

My counselor said, even with strong muscles, nobody can stop every bad thing that ever happens to them or to someone they love. She knows I wanted to help my mom. But I didn't know how.

She says kids aren't supposed to know how. She says we can't change what happens between other people, but we can change what we do.

Lots of people don't hit each other when they have angry feelings. I'm learning that I can use my words when I feel like fighting. I practice how with my counselor.

A Draw and Color Page

The world I see is different now. I miss my family but I don't miss the fights. I love my mom and dad but I didn't like what they did. They need to learn a lot before we can be together again. My counselor said it wasn't my fault. And that it was time for my mom and dad to get help.

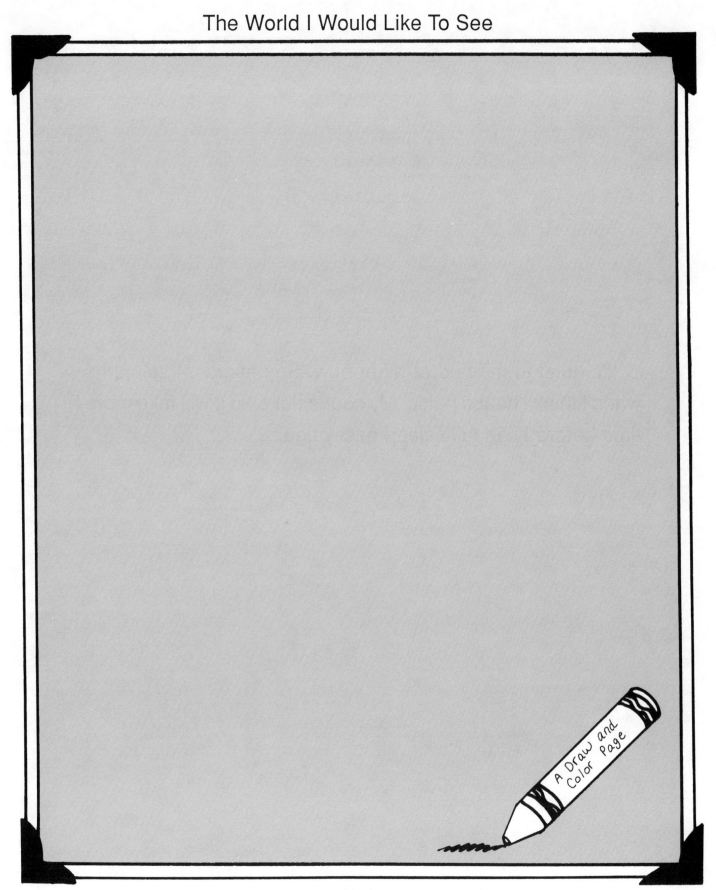

A Draw and Color Page

It's quiet in my bed at night now. Sometimes, I still jump when I think I hear a noise. My counselor said it will take more time before I can fall asleep easily again.

No one likes to be hurt and yelled at. A quiet house feels nice. When we're talking or laughing and feeling happy, a noisy house feels nice, too!

A Draw and Color Page

It can help to remember what's good about the world we live in. My counselor says when she remembers what's good about the world she sees, she thinks of me.

Something Good About My World

A Draw and Color Page

24